Ladybird Readers

G000298390

Knights and Castles
Activity Book

Written by Catrin Morris
Song lyrics on page 16 written by Pippa Mayfield
Illustrated by Alexandria Turner

 Singing *   Reading   Speaking   Critical thinking

 Spelling   Writing   🎧 Listening *

* To complete these activities, listen to tracks 2, 3, and 4 of the audio download available at **www.ladybird.com/ladybirdreaders**

Match the words to the pictures.

1 falcon

2 knight

3 lady

4 page

5 squire

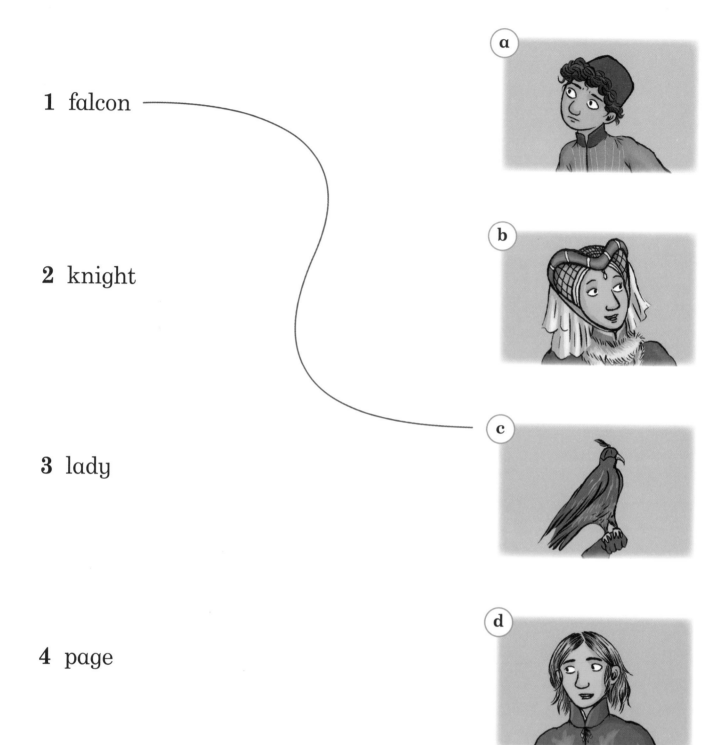

2 Look at the pictures. Write the correct words on the lines.

armor   cannon   tournament

hunting   jousting   castle

1

tournament

2

....

3

....

4

....

5

....

6

....

3 Circle the correct words.

1 night / (knight)

2 page / peige

3 castel / castle

4 amor / armor

5 falcon / folcan

6 sqwier / squire

4 Find the words.

h	t		f		n		j
u	c	u	e	l	f	s	p	u
n	t	a	r	d	c	u	r	a	s
i	i	r	n	i	o	h	t	g	t
n	n	m	a	w	n	e	t	e	i
g	o	m	c	a	n	n	o	n
o	r	e				l	h	g
d	d	r	n				a	f	x
f	j	t				d	v	d
y	r	s				y	s	p

tournament

cannon

page

jousting

lady

hunting

armor

falcon

5

5 Circle the correct pictures.

1 How did people find food?

2 Where did knights live?

3 What did knights wear to joust?

4 What did the knights' enemies use to break the castle wall?

5 Who helped the knight put his armor on?

6 **Listen and complete the sentences.** *

1 Where were the knights?

They were on ...._horses_......... .

2 Where was the squire?

He was in front of the

....

3 Where did the people live?

They lived in the

....

4 Where was the falcon?

It was flying near the

....

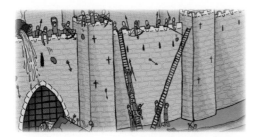

5 What were the enemies doing?

They were climbing up the

castle ....

6 What were the men doing?

They were standing behind

the ....

7 Ask and answer questions about the picture with a friend. 💬

1 What are the people in the picture doing?

The boy is standing on his hands. The woman and man are . . .

2 What are they wearing?

3 Which of these things do you do?

4 What do you wear to do it?

8 Put a ✓ by the things that were here 1,000 years ago. 📖 ❓

1 armor ✓

2 castle ☐

3 car ☐

4 computer ☐

5 fire ☐

6 jousting ☐

7 knight ☐

8 telephone ☐

9 bike ☐

9 **Circle the correct words.**

1 Knights had their own horses and armor, so they had to be **poor.** / **rich**.

2 It was very **easy** / **difficult** to learn jousting.

3 It was a **great** / **terrible** day when a squire was made a knight!

4 Enemies were **bad** / **good** people who wanted to break castle walls.

5 Knights and ladies liked wearing **cheap** / **expensive** clothes, so that other people knew they were rich.

6 It was hard for the knights' enemies to get inside **soft** / **strong** castles made of stone.

10 Look and read. Choose the correct words, and write them on the lines. 📖 ✏️

castle

clothes

fighting

Great Hall

hunting

wooden

1 Pages learned horse riding and .... *fighting* ....

2 When the squire was made a knight, he often had

his own ....

3 This stone castle is much stronger than the

.... castle.

4 Many ladies liked .... with falcons.

5 Everyone had meals together in the ....

6 Ladies made beautiful .... in the castle.

Look and write the letters.

| eat | emi | hti | nam | ann | unt | ode | oth | rid | ust |

1

tour...**nam**...ent

2

cl_____es

3

jo_____ing

4

horse _____ing

5

h_____ing

6

fig_____ng

7

c_____on

8

en_____es

9

Gr_____ Hall

10

wo_____n

12

12 Look and read. Choose the correct phrases and write them in the boxes. 📖 ✏️ ❓

| were boys | rode horses | were rich |

| learned to fight and ride horses | lived in castles |

| had their own castles | won tournaments |

| helped their fathers | ate in the Great Hall |

pages	knights and pages	knights
were boys		

13 Ask and answer questions about the picture with a friend. Use the words in the box.

sleep   work   eat   fly   help   live   hunt

Can it fly?

Yes, it can.

Does it hunt?

Yes, it does.

Is it a falcon?

Yes, it is!

14 **Listen and write complete answers.** *

1 How many knights are in the picture?

There are _____ two knights in the picture _____.

2 What are they doing?

They _____.

3 Where are they?

They _____.

4 Why are they jousting?

Because _____.

5 Who is winning?

The _____.

15 Sing the song. *

First, a boy was his father's page.
He learned to ride and fight.
Later, he left and became a squire,
and then became a knight.
A thousand years ago! A thousand years ago!

A knight often had his own castle.
The walls were made of stone.
His family and their animals lived
in a very strong home.
A thousand years ago! A thousand years ago!

In the Great Hall, they ate their meals.
Special food came from far away.
With horses and dogs and falcons,
they hunted for food every day.
A thousand years ago! A thousand years ago!

The family went inside the walls
when enemies came to the castle.
But cannons could break the very strong walls,
and that was the end of the castle.
Five hundred years ago! Five hundred years ago!

* To complete this activity, listen to track 4 of the audio download available at **www.ladybird.com/ladybirdreaders**